# Spac
# Plag

Written by David Orme

Illustrated by Aleksandar Sotirovski

FULL FLIGHT

# Titles in Full Flight 5

| | |
|---|---|
| Space Plague | Skyrunners |
| Bubble Attack | Spook Manor |
| Circus Scam | Dark Detective |
| Evil Brain Chips | Valley of Wisdom |
| Football Killers | Maxi Beasts |

Badger Publishing Limited
15 Wedgwood Gate, Pin Green Industrial Estate,
Stevenage, Hertfordshire SG1 4SU
Telephone: 01438 356907. Fax: 01438 747015
www.badger-publishing.co.uk
enquiries@badger-publishing.co.uk

Space Plague   ISBN 978 1 84691 118 7

Text © David Orme 2007
Complete work © Badger Publishing Limited 2007

Series Editor: Jonny Zucker
Publisher: David Jamieson
Commissioning Editor: Carrie Lewis
Editor: Paul Martin
Design: Fiona Grant
Illustration: Aleksander Sotirovski (Beehive Illustration)

Printed in China through Colorcraft Ltd., Hong Kong

# Space
# Plague

## How to use this book

In this book, YOU are the hero.
DO NOT read through from page to page!

You must choose your own route - but choose wisely or you will face great danger!

Turn over this page to begin.

Follow the 'Go to' prompts when you have chosen your route.

Good luck!

Space plague is spreading through the universe. For years scientists struggled to find a cure. But nothing worked. Now the plague is getting closer to Earth…

You are a space explorer. One day, you get a message on your space radio, but you don't hear all of it.

*"Can anyone hear us? This is the starship 888 Alpha. We think we've found the cure for space plague. You need to find… you'll need a code number…"*

Then the message stops.

A cure for space plague! You could save the human race. Your computer shows that the radio signal came from a solar system just ten light years away.

Straight away, you set your course…
**Go to 1**

**➡ 1** There are six planets in this solar system. Which one will you visit first?

The small, hot planet nearest the sun?
**Go to 2**
The jungle planet second from the sun?
**Go to 7**
The ocean planet third from the sun?
**Go to 16**
The desert planet fourth from the sun?
**Go to 41**
The gas giant fifth from the sun?
**Go to 6**
The ice world? **Go to 27**

➡ 2 You land on the small, hot planet. There is no atmosphere so you must wear your space suit. From space you noticed a place where spaceships had landed before. This is where you set down your space ship. There is a high cliff nearby, with a cave in it.

Will you explore the cave? Take care! The sun is rising. In four hours, the planet will be too hot to be safe!

Explore the cave? **Go to 18**
Take off and go to another planet?
**Go to 1**

➡ 3 You enter the building and find a door. But you need the code number to open it. What is the code number?

If you know and would like to try the door, go to that number.
Don't know the number?
**Go back to 7**

➡4 You are on the surface of the planet. Big mistake! The sun is high in the sky. No human can stand the heat for more than a few seconds. Sorry, mate, you're COOKED!
THE END

➡5 What's the point of an electric drill if there's nowhere to plug it in? You try and dig yourself out with your bare hands, but you starve to death before you can make it.
THE END

➡6 You cannot land on the gas giant, so you land on its only moon. You put on your space suit. A Guardian Robot is waiting at the entrance to a deep valley.

Approach the Guardian Robot?
**Go to 13**
Leave the moon and try somewhere else? **Go to 1**

➡7 The planet is completely covered with jungle except for a small clearing. At one side of the clearing is a building. The other way, a path disappears into the jungle.

What will you do?
Take off and go to another planet?
**Go to 1**
Explore the building? **Go to 3**
Try the path? **Go to 10**

➡ 8 This is the wrong answer, but you manage to run away from the Guardian Robot and return to your ship. **Go to 1**

➡ 9 Correct! There are two parents, plus six sons and one daughter.

The Guardian Robot stands aside. You enter the valley. A stone in the centre of the Valley has this carved on it:

$$22 - 1$$

and this strange mark:

$$\overline{\overline{\top}}$$

You now know the secret code number and symbol. This is vital information. Do not forget it!

You return to your spaceship. **Go to 1**

**10** You find some beautiful red plants. The seeds taste delicious!

Will you gather some of the seeds then return straight away to the clearing? **Go to 7**

Gather some seeds and carry on further up the path? **Go to 38**

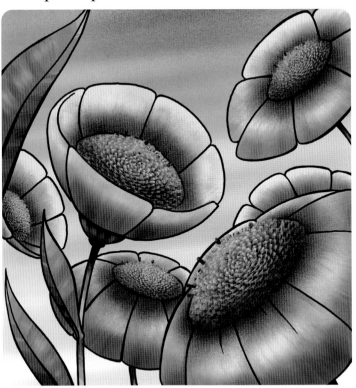

**→ 11** You are in a glass building on the desert planet. There is a computer and two doors. The doors are marked:

'ARRIVALS' and 'DEPARTURES'

These are transporters that can take you instantly to another planet in the solar system. You do not need to know the secret code to travel from here. But be careful – you may need it to get back again!

What will you do?
Switch on the computer? **Go to 40**
Go through the DEPARTURE door?
**Go to 20**

Leave the building and go to starship 888 Alpha, which is parked outside?
**Go to 17**

If you have arrived on this planet by space ship, you could leave the building and take off. **Go to 1**

➡ 12 Not far from your space ship you find a trap door. You open it and see a passage disappearing into darkness. Will you try it?

Yes? **Go to 29**
No? **Go to 25**

➡ 13 The Guardian Robot has a tough riddle for you. Are you up for it?

Yes? **Go to 30**
No? Go back to your space ship.
**Go to 1**

➡ 14 This is the wrong answer. The Guardian Robot imprisons you in a small cave. Your air supply is running out…
THE END

➡ **15** The passage ends in a door.
You need the code number to open it.
What is the code number?

If you know and would like to try the
door, go to that number.
If you don't **go back to 18**.

➡ **16** The ocean planet is covered with
ocean apart from one small island.
When you land on it, all you can see is
bare rock.

Will you explore the island? **Go to 12**
Take off and try another planet?
**Go to 1**

➡17 There is a sign on the starship.

SPACE PLAGUE. DO NOT ENTER UNLESS
YOU HAVE THE CURE.

You need three ingredients to be safe
from the plague: some seeds, a special
metal and a jewel. Each one comes from
a different planet.

Do you have all three ingredients?
Yes? **Go to 45**
No? You need to go back into the glass
building. Rush back before the door
closes behind you. **Go to 11**

➡18 The passage splits.

Which way will you choose?
The passage with smooth walls?
**Go to 15**
The passage with rough walls? **Go to 32**

→ 19 Sensible move. There are deadly meat-eaters in the jungle, but they only feed at night.

In the morning, you go for a walk and find red flowers with delicious tasting seeds. You gather some and return to the transporter.

But do you know the code?
If you know it, go to the code number.
If you don't, the creatures will get you when night comes!

You find a clue carved into the wall.
But what do you have to do with these
numbers to find the code?

$$
\begin{array}{r}
6 \\
5 \\
4 \\
3 \\
2 \\
1 \\
0 \\
\hline
? \\
\hline
\end{array}
$$

If you've worked out the code number,
go to that number.

If you haven't, you are going to be
dinner tonight!
THE END

➡20 There are three buttons on the wall of this space transporter. Each button has a picture on it. Which will you press?

An ocean. **Go to 36**
A hot sun. **Go to 39**
A jungle. **Go to 31**

If you decide not to travel in the transporter **go to 11**.

Be careful! If you travel from here, you may need a code to get back again!

➡21 THE DOOR OPENS!

You are in a transporter that moves you instantly from one planet to another in the solar system. You press a button. When the door opens again, you have **gone to 11**.

➡ **22** Sorry, the yellow dart gun is useless against these deadly creatures! You are doomed…
THE END

**➡ 23** You enter the building and find a door. But do you know the code to open it?

Yes? Go to the code number.
No? The meat-eaters have arrived - and guess who's going to be dinner?

Just then you see these numbers marked on the wall. What should you do with them to find the code?

6
5
4
3
2
1
0
___
?
___

Solved it? Go to it!
Not solved it? Oh dear...
THE END

➡ **24** This is the wrong answer. The Guardian Robot imprisons you in a small cave. Your air supply is running out…
THE END

➡ **25** Giant sea lizards with huge teeth come out of the water. Sadly, there is only one weapon that will defeat them – and you don't have one. They get closer and closer…
THE END

➡ **26** You find a place where the passage divides. One way goes to the surface of the planet. The other way is a rough passage. Which will you choose?

The surface? **Go to 4**
The rough passage? **Go to 44**

➡ **27** The ice world is a horrible place. Unless you are well protected, the freezing air will kill you. There is nothing here but storms and ice and death.

What will you do?
Land anyway? **Go to 37**
Try another planet? **Go to 1**

➡ **28** You return to planet Earth a hero. You have saved the human race and succeeded in your mission.
THE END

**➡ 29** At the end of the passage is a door. You can only open it if you have found out the code.

If you know the code and would like to try the door, go to the code number.
If not, climb out of the trapdoor.
**Go to 25**

➡**30** Here is the riddle the Guardian Robot asks you:

A MOTHER AND FATHER HAVE SIX SONS AND EACH SON HAS ONE SISTER. HOW MANY PEOPLE ARE IN THAT FAMILY?

8? **Go to 8**
9? **Go to 9**
14? **Go to 14**

➡31 You arrive at the jungle planet. The transporter is in a building. You look outside the building. It is the middle of the night here.

What do you do?
Go and look around in the dark?
**Go to 43**
Stay in the transporter until morning?
**Go to 19**

➡32 The passage comes to an end. You find some strange yellow metal that looks like gold. Gather some up and put it in your pocket. It may be useful!

Suddenly, there is a rumble and a rock fall behind you makes you run for cover. It takes many hours to dig your way out. The sun has risen and the surface of the planet has melted. Your space ship has vanished!

You try the other passage, but there's a difficult problem to solve… **Go to 34**

➡**33** Oh dear! This door leads to the laboratory where space plague was studied many years ago. The plague has escaped into the room and you catch it…
THE END

➡**34** The passage ends in a door. You can only open it if you have found out the code.

At last, in a dark corner, you find a clue to the code… but what is the missing number?

## 1 1 2 3 5 8 13 … 34

If you know the code and would like to try the door, go to the code number.
If you can't work it out, **go to 4**.

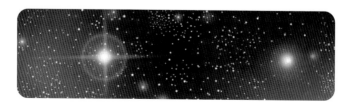

**35** Good choice. The drill would have been useless. Dig yourself out and head for the transporter. Go to the code number.

Don't know the code? You find a clue carved into the wall. But what is the missing number?

1 1 2 3 5 8 13 … 34

Solved it? Go to the code number.
Can't work it out? Try the surface of the planet. **Go to 4**

**36** You are on the ocean planet. Here you will need to fight some giant lizards! Before you leave the transporter, you find a purple ray gun and a yellow dart gun.

They are heavy and you can only choose one of them. Choose now:
✳ Purple ray gun? **Go to 42**
✳ Yellow dart gun? **Go to 22**

➡️ **37** We told you there was nothing here but wind and ice and death, so what did you land for? Sorry, you're dead – very dead.
THE END

➡️ **38** You walk into the lair of some giant spiders. You get stuck in a web. It takes you hours to free yourself. When you return to the clearing, it is night time. To your horror, the clearing is full of hungry meat-eating monsters. They have smashed your space ship beyond repair.

Your only hope is the building.
**Go to 23**

➡️ **39** You are on the hot planet, nearest the sun. Inside the transporter there is a pickaxe and a powerful electric drill. You can only carry one.

Which one will you choose?
Carry the one you have chosen to **26**.

➡ **40** You switch on the computer. A message has been left by the ancient people that once lived in this solar system.

To make the cure, you need three ingredients:
* Seeds of the red plant from the jungle planet.
* Jewels from the lizards on the ocean planet.
* Yellow metal from the hot planet.

You need to gather up any ingredients that you don't already have.
To do this, go to the departure door.
**Go to 20**

Remember, if you haven't found the secret code yet, you may not be able to get back!

If you have arrived on this planet by space ship, you could try and use that to collect the ingredients instead. **Go to 1**

➡ **41** On the desert planet is the starship 888 Alpha. The ship is in working order, but the crew are dead. On the airlock door is a notice:

SPACE PLAGUE. DO NOT ENTER UNLESS YOU HAVE THE CURE.

You carry on past the ship to a huge glass building. There are two doors. Each has a symbol on it.

Which door will you open?
The door with:
**Go to 11**

The door with:
**Go to 33**

➡️ **42** Good choice. You leave the transporter and climb through a trapdoor. The lizards are waiting. Luckily you have the right weapon. You do what you have to do.

Each lizard has a beautiful jewel on its head. You gather some and put them in your pocket.

Your weapon runs out of power, so you rush back to the transporter before more lizards appear.

If you know the code number, go to that page.

If you don't have the code number, you will have to stay on the planet. Soon more lizards will come and eat you. I did tell you that you needed the code number...

THE END

➡43 This was a really bad idea. The jungle is full of meat-eating animals that get very hungry in the night – and guess who's on the menu?
THE END

➡44 You follow the rough passage. You find some yellow metal that looks like gold. You put some in your pocket but, just as you are picking up another pocketful, the roof falls in. You must dig yourself out.

What did you bring?
Pickaxe? **Go to 35**
Electric drill? **Go to 5**

➡45 You enter the space ship and discover the fate of the crew. Nasty thing, space plague! Good job you have the cure! Take off and set course for Planet Earth. **Go to 28.**